ALL-TIME GREATEST LOVE SONGS

38 ROMANTIC CLASSICS ARRANGED FOR PIANO, VOICE & GUITAR

ALL-TIME GREATEST LOVE SONGS

38 ROMANTIC CLASSICS ARRANGED FOR PIANO, VOICE & GUITAR

Wise Publications
London/New York/Paris/Sydney/Copenhagen/Madrid

EXCLUSIVE DISTRIBUTORS:

MUSIC SALES LIMITED
8/9 FRITH STREET,
LONDON W1V 5TZ, ENGLAND.

MUSIC SALES PTY LIMITED
120 ROTHSCHILD AVENUE,
ROSEBERY, NSW 2018, AUSTRALIA.

ORDER NO. AM943998
ISBN 0-7119-6572-2
THIS BOOK © COPYRIGHT 1997
BY WISE PUBLICATIONS

BOOK DESIGN BY FROST DESIGN
COMPILED BY PETER EVANS

PHOTOGRAPHS COURTESY OF
HENRIK KNUDSEN

YOUR GUARANTEE OF QUALITY:
AS PUBLISHERS, WE STRIVE TO PRODUCE
EVERY BOOK TO THE HIGHEST
COMMERCIAL STANDARDS. THIS BOOK
HAS BEEN CAREFULLY DESIGNED TO
MINIMISE AWKWARD PAGE TURNS AND
TO MAKE PLAYING FROM IT A REAL
PLEASURE. PARTICULAR CARE HAS BEEN
GIVEN TO SPECIFYING ACID-FREE,
NEUTRAL-SIZED PAPER MADE FROM PULPS
WHICH HAVE NOT BEEN ELEMENTAL
CHLORINE BLEACHED. THIS PULP IS FROM
FARMED SUSTAINABLE FORESTS AND WAS
PRODUCED WITH SPECIAL REGARD FOR
THE ENVIRONMENT. THROUGHOUT, THE
PRINTING AND BINDING HAVE BEEN
PLANNED TO ENSURE A STURDY,
ATTRACTIVE PUBLICATION WHICH
SHOULD GIVE YEARS OF ENJOYMENT. IF
YOUR COPY FAILS TO MEET OUR HIGH
STANDARDS, PLEASE INFORM US AND WE
WILL GLADLY REPLACE IT.

MUSIC SALES' COMPLETE CATALOGUE
DESCRIBES THOUSANDS OF TITLES AND IS
AVAILABLE IN FULL COLOUR SECTIONS BY
SUBJECT, DIRECT FROM MUSIC SALES
LIMITED. PLEASE STATE YOUR AREAS OF
INTEREST AND SEND A CHEQUE/POSTAL
ORDER FOR £1.50 FOR POSTAGE TO:
MUSIC SALES LIMITED
NEWMARKET ROAD, BURY ST. EDMUNDS,
SUFFOLK IP33 3YB.

AIN'T NO MOUNTAIN HIGH ENOUGH

WORDS & MUSIC BY NICKOLAS ASHFORD & VALERIE SIMPSON

Verse 2.
I set you free
I told you you could always count on me
From that day on, I made a vow,
I'll be there when you want me,
Some way, some how,
'Cause baby there *(Chorus)*

Verse 3.
My love is alive
Way down in my heart
Although we are miles apart
If you ever need a helping hand,
I'll be there on the double
As fast as I can.
Don't you know that there *(Chorus)*

ALL FOR LOVE

WORDS & MUSIC BY BRYAN ADAMS,
ROBERT JOHN 'MUTT' LANGE & MICHAEL KAMEN

9

ALWAYS

WORDS & MUSIC BY JONATHAN LEWIS, DAVID LEWIS & WAYNE LEWIS

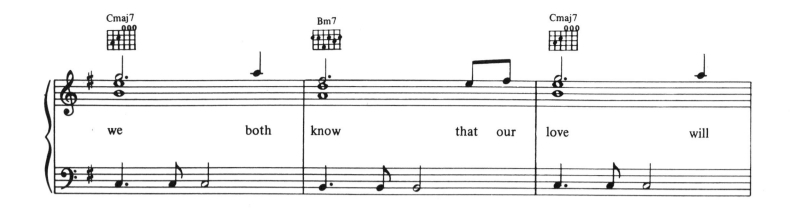

we both know that our love will

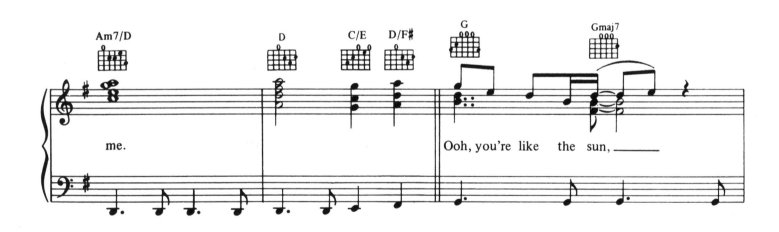

grow and for - ev - er it will be you and

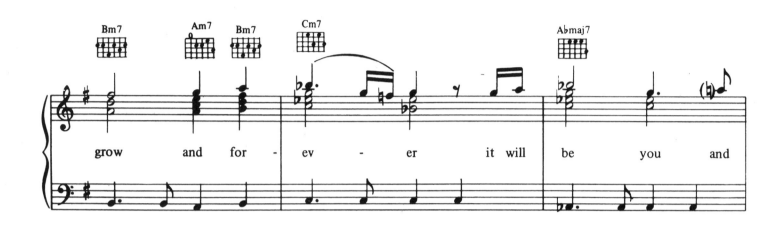

me. Ooh, you're like the sun, _____

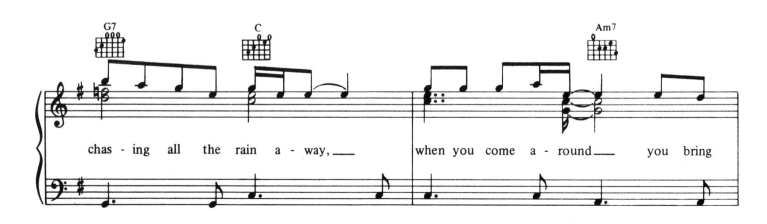

chas - ing all the rain a - way, _____ when you come a - round _____ you bring

VERSE 2:
Come with me my sweet
Let's go make a family
And they will bring us joy for always.

Oh boy I love you so
I can't find enough ways to let you know
But you can be sure I'm yours for always.

AND I LOVE HER

WORDS & MUSIC BY JOHN LENNON & PAUL McCARTNEY

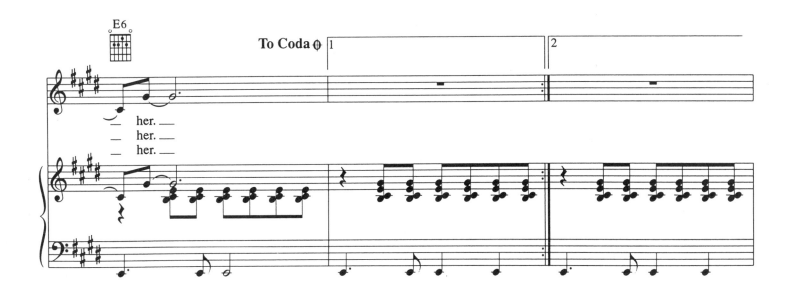

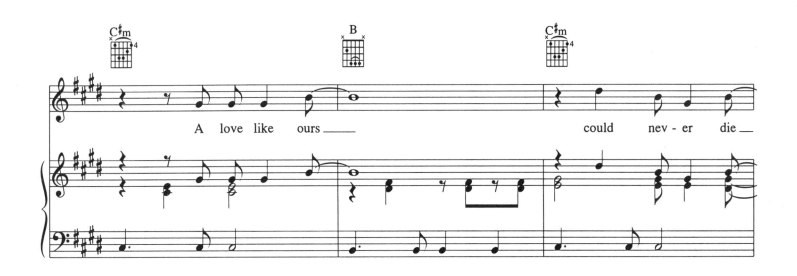

will nev-er die. ___ And I love ___ her. ___

AND I LOVE YOU SO

WORDS & MUSIC BY DON McLEAN

ANGEL EYES (HOME AND AWAY)

MUSIC BY CLARK, CUNNINGHAM, MITCHELL & PELLOW
WORDS BY CLARK, CUNNINGHAM, MITCHELL, PELLOW & CHRIS DIFFORD

D.%.al Coda

⊕ Coda

(Repeat 4 times)

And with ____ those an - gel eyes. ____

(ad lib.) Ev'rything's gonna be all right now baby.

Verse 2:
The saddest thing I've ever seen on my TV screen
Was a dying man who died for his dream
The toughest thing I've ever heard
Was that newborn scream in this naked world.

ANNIE'S SONG

WORDS & MUSIC BY JOHN DENVER

ANYONE WHO HAD A HEART

WORDS BY HAL DAVID
MUSIC BY BURT BACHARACH

Very slowly

hurt me ___ like you hurt me, and be so un -

true. What am I to do? ___

Ev - 'ry time you go a - way ___ I al - ways say, ___

___ This time it's good - bye, dear.

Lov-ing you the way I do, _____ I take you back; _____

With-out you I'd die, dear. Know-ing I love you

so. An-y-one who had a heart would

take me _____ in his arms and _____ love me

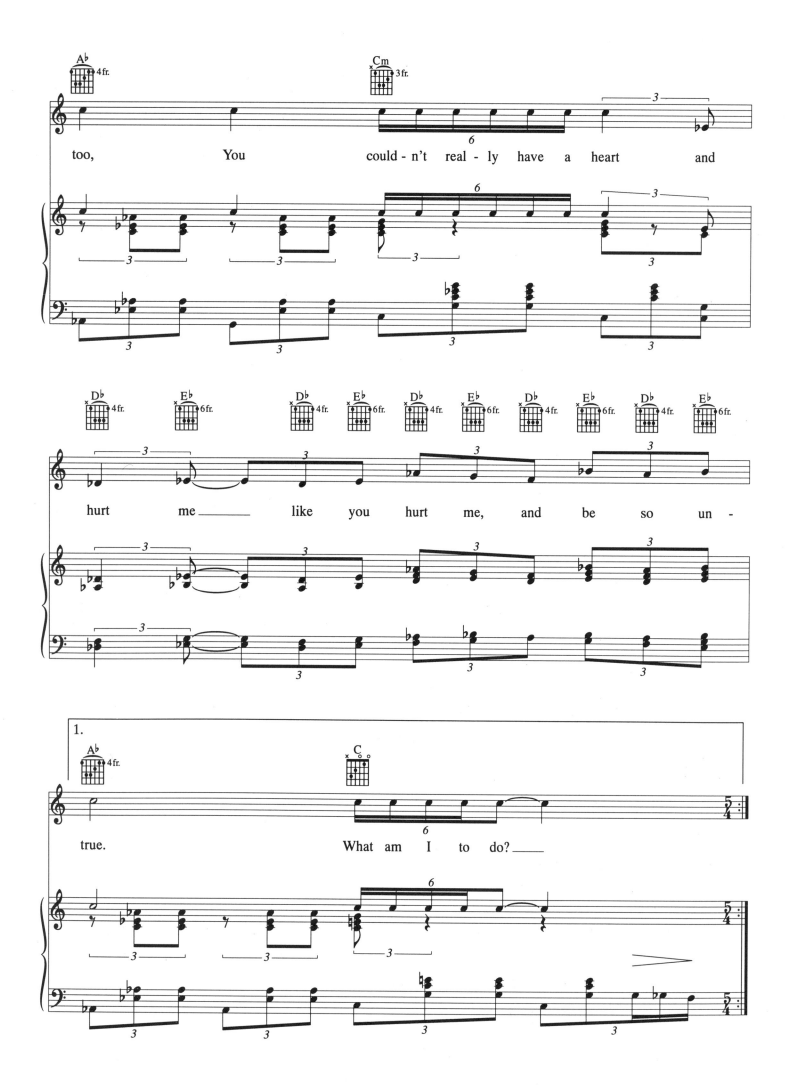

COULD IT BE MAGIC

WORDS & MUSIC BY BARRY MANILOW & ADRIENNE ANDERSON

- der   of   all ___ of you.
- ic   at   last? _____

Ba - by   I   want ___ you.

ENDLESS LOVE

WORDS & MUSIC BY LIONEL RICHIE

ETERNAL FLAME

WORDS & MUSIC BY BILLY STEINBERG, TOM KELLY & SUSANNA HOFFS

Close your eyes, give me your hand, darling.
I believe it's meant to be, darling.

Do you feel my heart beating, do you understand?
I want you when you are sleeping, you belong to me.

life so lone - ly___ and then come and ease___ the pain.___

I don't wan- na lose this feel – ing, oh.

oh.

D.S. 𝄉 al Coda ⊕
(lyric 1)

49

FALLING INTO YOU

WORDS & MUSIC BY RICK NOWLES, MARIE-CLAIRE D'UBALIO & BILLY STEINBERG

HOW DEEP IS YOUR LOVE

WORDS & MUSIC BY BARRY GIBB, ROBIN GIBB & MAURICE GIBB

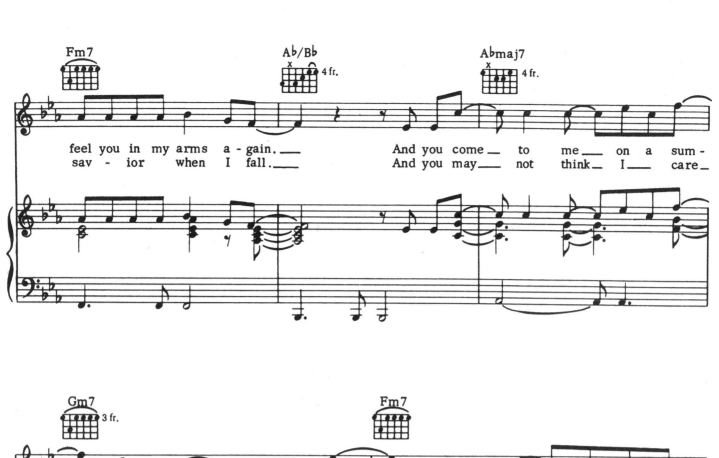

feel you in my arms a-gain.___ And you come___ to me___ on a sum-
sav - ior when I fall.___ And you may___ not think I___ care

mer breeze;___ keep me warm___ in your love,___ then you soft-
— for you___ when you know___ down in-side___ that I real-

ly leave.—
ly do.___ } And it's me you need___ to show: ___ How deep___

how deep is your love.

HARD TO SAY I'M SORRY

WORDS & MUSIC BY P. CETERA & D. FOSTER

To Coda

60

Verse 2:
Couldn't stand to be kept away
Not for a day from your body
Wouldn't want to be swept away
Far away from the one that I love.

Hold me now
It's hard for me to say I'm sorry
I just want you to know.

HAVE I TOLD YOU LATELY?

WORDS & MUSIC BY VAN MORRISON

Moderately slow

63

VERSE 2:

Oh the morning sun in all its glory
Greets the day with hope and comfort too
And you fill my life with laughter
You can make it better
Ease my troubles that's what you do.

VERSE 3: — as Verse 1

VERSE 4: — Instrumental

MIDDLE:

There's a love that's divine
And it's yours and it's mine
And it shines like the sun
At the end of the day
We will give thanks and pray to the one.

VERSE 5: — as Verse 1

I AM BLESSED

WORDS & MUSIC BY MARSHA MALAMET & MARK MUELLER

Verse 2:
So many changes
This world can put you through.
Sometimes it's hard to find a way,
A heart can get confused
But then I hold you and it all falls into place,
You give me what's right and I cannot erase.
So when I'm feeling down
I feel sorry for myself,
I look around and it's easy to tell.

I CAN'T STOP LOVING YOU

WORDS & MUSIC BY DON GIBSON

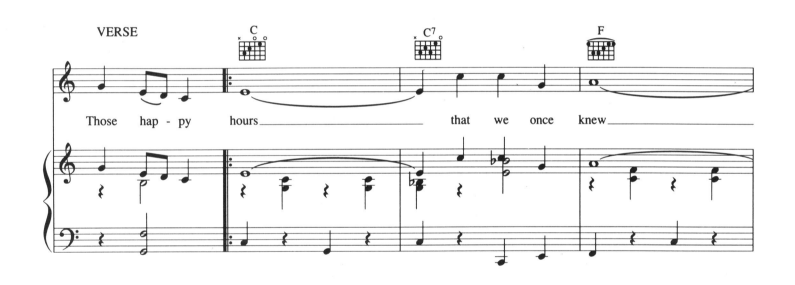

Those hap-py hours _____ that we once knew _____

_____ though long a-go _____ they still make me blue.

They say that time _____ heals a bro-ken heart, _____ but time has stood still _____ since we've been a- -part. _____ I can't stop lov-ing you, _____ I've made up my mind _____ to live in

I JUST WANT TO
MAKE LOVE TO YOU

WORDS & MUSIC BY WILLIE DIXON

tell by the way____ you walk____ that walk, and I can

hear by the way____ you____ talk____ that talk, and I can

know by the way____ you____ treat____ your girl that I could

give you all the lov - in' in the whole wide world.

Verse 2:

All I want to do is wash your clothes
I don't want to keep you indoors
There is nothing for you to do but
Keep me making love to you.

Verse 3:

All I want to do is make your bread
Just to make sure you're well fed
I don't want you sad and blue
I just want to make love to you.

Verse 4:

All I want to do is cook your bread
Just to make sure you're well fed
I don't want you sad and blue
And I just want to make love to you.

(JUST LIKE) STARTING OVER

WORDS & MUSIC BY JOHN LENNON

love _____ a - gain. It - 'll be just like start - ing
by, _____ my love. It - 'll be just like start - ing

o - - - ver, start - ing
o - - - ver, start - ing

To Coda ⊕ **1.**

o - - - ver. ____ Ev - 'ry
o - - - ver. ____

2.

N.C.

Why don't we take off a -

lone, ___ take a trip some-where far,

far a - way. ___ We'll be to - geth - er all a -

lone ___ a - gain, like we used to ___ in the

D.%. (lyric 1) al Coda

ear - ly days. ___ Well, well, dar - lin'. It's

Although our love is still spe-cial,

let's take a chance and fly a-way some-where.

Repeat (vocal ad lib.) and fade

IT'S IMPOSSIBLE
(SOMOS NOVIOS)

WORDS BY SID WAYNE
MUSIC BY A. MANZANERO

Chorus:

It's Im-pos-si-ble, Tell the sun to leave the sky, It's just im-pos-si-ble,

It's Im-pos-si-ble, Ask a ba-by not to cry, It's just im-

pos-si-ble. Can I hold you ___ clos-er to me, ___ and not

KILLING ME SOFTLY WITH HIS SONG

WORDS BY NORMAN GIMBEL
MUSIC BY CHARLES FOX

I heard he sang___ a good song   I___ heard he had a style___
I felt all flushed___ with fe-ver   em-bar-rassed by the crowd___
He sang as if___ he knew me   in___ all my dark des-pair___

Bbm7   Eb   Ab   Db

And so I came___ to see him   and list-en for___ a while___
I felt he found___ my let-ters   and read each one___ out loud___
And then he looked___ right through me   as if I was-n't there___

Bbm7   Eb   Fm   C7sus4 Fm

And there___ he was___ this young___ boy   a stran-ger to my eyes___
I prayed___ that he___ would fin-ish   but he just kept right on___
But he___ was there___ this strang-er   sing-ing clear and strong___

Bbm7   Eb7   Ab   C7

Strumming my pain___ with his fin-gers___   sing-ing my life___ with his words___

Fm   Bbm   Eb7

88

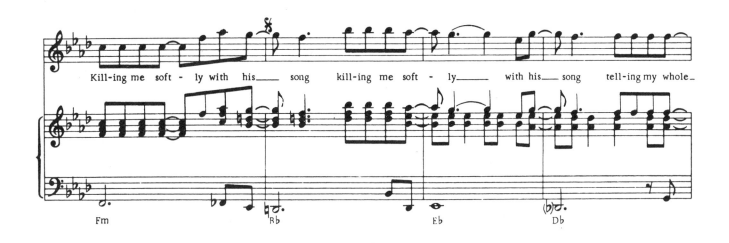

Kill-ing me soft - ly with his song kill-ing me soft-ly with his song tell-ing my whole

Fm   Bb   Eb   Db

To Coda ⊕

life with his words Kill - ing me soft - ly with his song

Ab   Db   Gb

1-2   3

He was strum-ming there yea he was sing -

F   Fm   Bbm

D. S. al Coda   ⊕ *CODA*

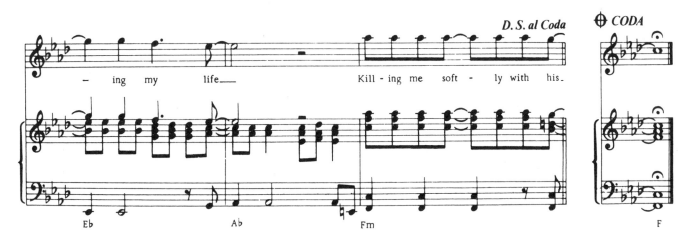

- ing my life Kill - ing me soft - ly with his

Eb   Ab   Fm   F

LOVIN' YOU

WORDS & MUSIC BY MINNIE RIPERTON & RICHARD RUDOLPH

Lov - in' you _____ is ea - sy 'cause you're beau - ti - ful,

OCEAN DRIVE

WORDS & MUSIC BY PAUL TUCKER

1. Say it's true, pink and blue,— I can share— your— sit-u-a-
(Verse 2 see block lyric)

Verse 2:
He left you black and blue
Without a word of explanation.
And he took your love for granted
And he left you high and dry.
And you know someday
Well you'll wonder what you see in him anyway.
When that day arrives
We'll live on Ocean Drive.

ONE MOMENT IN TIME

WORDS & MUSIC BY ALBERT HAMMOND & JOHN BETTIS

NO MORE 'I LOVE YOU'S'

WORDS & MUSIC BY D. FREEMAN & J. HUGHES

do do do.
1. I used to be lu - na - tic   from the   gra - cious days.
(Verse 2 see block lyric)

I   used   to be woe - be - gone____

and   so   rest - less nights.   My   ach - ing   heart____

____ would bleed____   for you____ to see.____   Oh____ but

now _____

I don't find my-self bounc-ing home, whis-tl-ing but-ton hole tunes to make_ me

cry, no more "I love you's" a lan-guage is leav-

-ing me. No more "I love you's"

chang-es are shift-ing out-side_ the words.

(The lo-ver speaks a-bout the mon-sters.) Do bi do bi

A lan-guage is leav-ing me in si-lence. No more "I

love you's" chan-ges are shift-ing out-side the words.

106

Verse 2:
I used to have demons in my room at night
Desire, despair, desire, so many monsters.
Oh, but now
I don't find myself bouncing home
Whistling buttonhole tunes to make me cry.

SO AMAZING

WORDS & MUSIC BY LUTHER VANDROSS

SOMETHING'S GOTTEN HOLD OF MY HEART

WORDS & MUSIC BY ROGER COOK & ROGER GREENAWAY

(1.3.) Some-thing's got-ten hold of my heart ___ keep-ing my soul ___ and my sen-ses a-part.
(2.4.) Some-thing's got-ten hold of my hand ___ dragg-ing my soul ___ to a beau-ti-ful land.

___ (1.3.)
___ (2.4.) (Yeah ___)

Some-thing's got-ten in-to my life ___ cut-ting its
Some-thing has in-va-ded my night ___ paint-ing my

113

SUNNY

WORDS & MUSIC BY BOBBY HEBB

119

THE WIND BENEATH MY WINGS

WORDS & MUSIC BY JEFF SILBAR & LARRY HENLEY

I nev-er once__ heard you com-plain.

Did you ev-er know__ that you're my__ he-ro,

and ev-'ry-thing__ I'd like to be?

I can fly high-er than an ea - gle,__

'cause you are the wind____ be-neath my wings.

It might have ap - peared____ to go un -

no - ticed that I've got it all____ here in my

heart.

I want you to know____ I know the

TO LOVE SOMEBODY

WORDS & MUSIC BY BARRY GIBB & ROBIN GIBB

There's a light, a cer-tain kind of light
brain I see your face a-gain;

that nev-er shone on me.
I know my frame of mind.

I want my life to
You ain't got to be so

UNCHAINED MELODY

MUSIC BY ALEX NORTH
WORDS BY HY ZARET

UP WHERE WE BELONG

WORDS & MUSIC BY JACK NITZSCHE, WILL JENNINGS & BUFFY SAINTE MARIE

Until It's Time For You To Go

WORDS & MUSIC BY BUFFY SAINTE-MARIE

WITHOUT YOU

WORDS & MUSIC BY PETER HAM & TOM EVANS

think of all my sor-row and I had you there but then I let you go. And now it's

on-ly fair that I should let you know what you should know: _____ I can't

Chorus: *(2nd time, 8va higher till *)*

live, _____ if liv-ing is with-out you, _____ I can't live, I can't

give an-y-more.___ I can't live _____ if liv-ing is with-out you, _____ I can't

WONDERFUL TONIGHT

WORDS & MUSIC BY ERIC CLAPTON

1. It's late in the eve - ning,
2. We go to a par - ty,
3. It's time to go home — now,

she's won-d'ring what clothes _ to wear. _ She puts on her make-
and ev - 'ry-one turns _ to see _ this beau-ti-ful la -
and I've got an ach - ing head. _ So I give her the car _

And then she asks ___ me, "Do I look all right?"
And then she asks ___ me, "Do you feel all right?"
And then I tell ___ her, as I turn out the light,

And I say "Yes, you look won-der-ful ___ to-night."
And I say "Yes, I feel won-der-ful ___ to-night."
I say, "My dar-ling, you are won-der-ful ___ to-night."

YOU ARE NOT ALONE

WORDS & MUSIC BY ROBERT KELLY

1. An-oth-er day— has gone,— I'm still all— a-lone— how could— this be,— you're not here— with me..

(Verses 2, 3 & 4 see block lyric)

You ne-ver said— good-bye,— some-one tell— me why,— did she have— to go

why— lone.————— (3.) Just the oth - er night—

but you are not— a-lone.——— Whis-per— three words— then I'll— come

run - ning, I— and girl— you know— that I'll— be

there, I'll be there. You are not— a- lone,—

150

Verse 2:

You are not alone
I am here with you
Though you're far away
I am here to stay.
You are not alone
I am here with you
Though we're far apart
You're always in my heart.
But you are not alone.

Verse 3:

Just the other night
I thought I heard you cry
Asking me to go
And hold you in my arms.
I can hear your breaths
Your burdens I will bear
But first I need you here
Then forever can begin.

Verse 4:

You are not alone
I am here with you
Though you're far away
I am here to stay.
But you are not alone
I am here with you
Though we're far apart
You're always in my heart.
But you are not alone.

YOU MUST LOVE ME

MUSIC BY ANDREW LLOYD WEBBER
LYRICS BY TIM RICE

lieved— in you.— Cer - tain - ties dis - ap -

pear what do we do— for our dream to sur - vive,

how do we keep— all our pas-sions a - live as we used to do?—

Deep in my heart I'm con - ceal - ing

Verse 2: (Instrumental 8 bars)
Why are you at my side?
How can I be any use to you now?
Give me a chance and I'll let you see how
Nothing has changed.
Deep in my heart I'm concealing
Things that I'm longing to say,
Scared to confess what I'm feeling
Frightened you'll slip away,
You must love me.

YOUR SONG

WORDS & MUSIC BY ELTON JOHN AND BERNIE TAUPIN

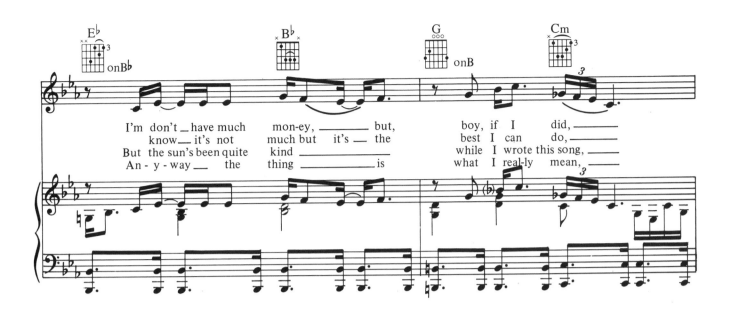

I'm don't _ have much mon-ey, _____ but,
know _ it's not much but it's _ the
But the sun's been quite kind _____
An - y-way _ the thing _____ is

boy, if I did, _____
best I can do, _____
while I wrote this song, _____
what I real-ly mean, _

I'd buy _ a big house where _____ we both could live.
My gift is my song and _____ keep it _ turned on.
It's for peo-ple like you, that _____
Yours are the sweet-est eyes _____

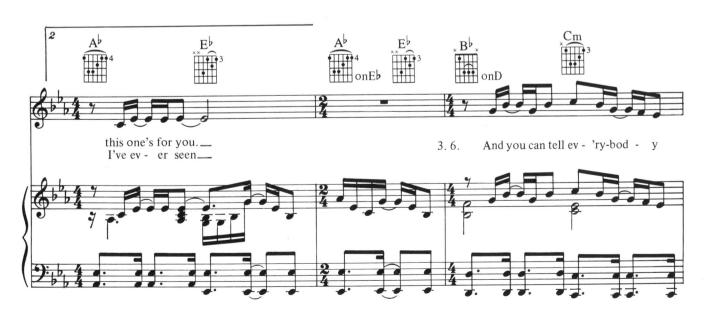

this one's for you. _
I've ev - er seen _

3. 6.   And you can tell ev - 'ry-bod - y

7.8. I hope you don't mind, — I hope you don't mind ——— that I put — down in — words, How

won - der - ful life is— while you're— in — the world.—

rit.

a tempo

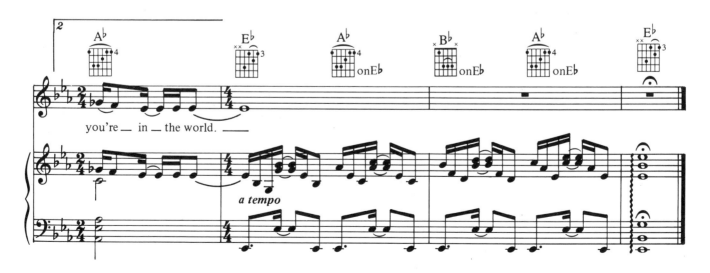

you're — in — the world. ——

a tempo